# FATCAT...

*Dedicated to Tom.*
*Definitely not Jerry.*

# FATCAT...

*How to be Slim, Trim ... Purrfect*

## Tony Husband

Thorsons
*An Imprint of HarperCollinsPublishers*

Thorsons
An Imprint of HarperCollins*Publishers*
77–85 Fulham Palace Road,
Hammersmith, London W6 8JB
1160 Battery Street
San Francisco, California 94111–1213

Published by Thorsons 1996
1 3 5 7 9 10 8 6 4 2

A catalogue record for this book
is available from the British Library

ISBN 0 7225 3297 0

Printed and bound in Great Britain by
Woolnough Bookbinding Limited, Irthlingborough

Sometimes being
overweight provokes sarcasm.

Oi! Fatso ... lose weight!!

Most cats have nine lives.
Fat cats have nine chins.

Weight-watching can be fun.

Don't forget –
the mirror sometimes lies.

Choose your role models carefully.

Try hare-obics.

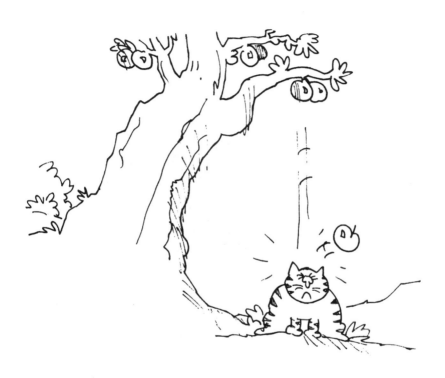

An apple a day...

Cycling can be an
exhilarating experience.

Try to walk rather than use the car.

Don't be a TV couch potato.

Take a bracing walk by the sea.

Dancing is an
enjoyable way to exercise.

Don't be lazy, use your legs.

Exercise those limbs.

Climbing is good for muscle-building.

A stroll in the countryside
keeps your heart healthy.

Weight-watchers
should watch those weights.

Avoid steroids, however
you might be tempted.

Develop your arm
muscles with lift-ups.

Limber up before you exercise.

Trampolining has its rewards.

Exercise machines
should be used with care.

Try taking up a new sport.

Jogging is a great way to keep trim.

Skipping keeps you fit and it's fun.

Stretching can help cure backache.

Yoga heals mind, body and spirit.

Avoid keep fit exercises
on TV... You might fall off.

Choose your personal
trainer with care.

Always shower after exercising.

Try a mud bath as a revitalizer.

Bathing in milk
keeps you soft and supple.

Too many diet books
can only confuse you.

Don't get in a flap
if your diet's not working.

Crash diets are not recommended.

Beware of chocolate.

Hot dogs are unhealthy.

Fast food is not a sensible choice.

Shellfish may not agree with everyone.

Free range is usually the best option.

Basket meals are to be avoided.

Sharing a meal can be a sociable
way of halving the calories.

Frozen food is convenient.
Just make sure you unfreeze it first.

Avoid sweets.

Bran can have its drawbacks.

White meat is better for you.

Not all food is friendly to your system.

A sweet tooth can get you into trouble.

Boiled fish makes a healthy meal.

Cut down on dairy products.

Pasta is excellent for
carbohydrate loading.

Don't be reluctant to take vitamins.

Eat more fruit.

Eating out may be fun
but it does nothing for your diet.

Greens are normally good for you.

A little red wine daily can be healthy.

Always aim for a balanced diet.

Beware those sneaky midnight feasts.